OCTOBER SKY

by
Homer H. Hickam, Jr.

Student Packet

Written by
Pat Watson

Edited by
Heather M. Johnson

Contains masters for: 2 Prereading Activities
4 Vocabulary Activities
1 Complete Study Guide
5 Literary Analysis Activities
3 Comprehension Activities
4 Unit Quizzes
2 Final Tests (Two Levels)
PLUS   Detailed Answer Key

Note

The Dell paperback edition of the book, ©1998 by Homer H. Hickam, Jr., was used to prepare this guide. The page references may differ in other editions.

Please note: This novel deals with sensitive, mature issues. Parts may contain profanity, sexual references, and/or descriptions of violence. Please assess the appropriateness of this book for the age level and maturity of your students prior to reading and discussing it with them.

Copyright infringement is a violation of Federal Law.

© 2003 by Novel Units, Inc., San Antonio, Texas. All rights reserved. No part of this publication may be reproduced, translated, stored in a retrieval system, or transmitted in any way or by any means (electronic, mechanical, photocopying, recording, or otherwise) without prior written permission from ECS Learning Systems, Inc.

Photocopying of student worksheets by a classroom teacher at a non-profit school who has purchased this publication for his/her own class is permissible. Reproduction of any part of this publication for an entire school or for a school system, by for-profit institutions and tutoring centers, or for commercial sale is strictly prohibited.

Novel Units is a registered trademark of Novel Units, Inc.

Printed in the United States of America.

To order, contact your local school supply store, or—

Novel Units, Inc.
P.O. Box 791610
San Antonio, TX 78279

Web site: www.educyberstor.com

Name _____

Clue Search

Directions: Collect information about the book for each of the items. Write down the information and then make some predictions about the book.

Information Source	Information Provided
Dedication	
Title	
Cover Illustration	
Teasers on the cover	
Friends' recommendations	
Reviewers' recommendations/awards won	

Your predictions about the book:

Directions: Complete the following chart for the word *perseverance.*

Synonyms	Antonyms
_____	_____
_____	_____
_____	_____

PERSEVERANCE

Results of perseverance	People you know who have this trait
_____	_____
_____	_____
_____	_____

Name _____

October Sky
Activity #3 • Vocabulary
Chapters 1–5, pp. 1–87

enthalpy (1)	kinetic (1)	bituminous coal (1)	sonorous (4)
pristine (7)	tipple (11)	precipitously (26)	prowess (33)
proclivity (33)	inexorable (39)	molecule (39)	impotent (55)
entity (62)	surreptitiously (65)	oxidizer (74)	succinctly (77)
insidious (78)	cohesiveness (78)	saltpeter (79)	casement (83)

Directions: Write each vocabulary word in the left-hand column of the chart. Complete the chart by placing a check mark in the column that best describes your familiarity with each word. Working with a partner, find and read the line in which each word appears in the story. Find the meaning of each word in the dictionary. Together with your partner, choose ten of the words checked in the last column. On a separate sheet of paper, use each of those words in a sentence.

Vocabulary Word	I Can Define	I Have Seen/Heard	New Word For Me

All rights reserved

© Novel Units, Inc.   5

nefarious (94)	propellant (98)	prodigious (100)	pernicious (104)
cupidity (105)	cogitative (106)	subjective (119)	rabble-rouser (121)
petulance (124)	ballistic missile (129)	debacle (136)	polyhedron (152)
ironic (162)	deductive (169)	infinity (169)	coalescing (170)
primordial (184)	viscous (186)	slurry (187)	theodolite (190)
methane (194)			

Directions: Match each word with the word or phrase closest in meaning.

____ 1. nefarious

____ 2. propellant

____ 3. prodigious

____ 4. pernicious

____ 5. cupidity

____ 6. cogitative

____ 7. subjective

____ 8. rabble-rouser

____ 9. petulance

____ 10. ballistic missile

____ 11. debacle

____ 12. polyhedron

____ 13. ironic

____ 14. deductive

____ 15. infinity

____ 16. coalescing

____ 17. primordial

____ 18. viscous

____ 19. slurry

____ 20. theodolite

____ 21. methane

a. thoughtful, meditative

b. inferable

c. villainous

d. disaster

e. semi-fluid

f. tremendous

g. testiness

h. a solid figure having four or more faces

i. endless

j. colorless, odorless, flammable gas

k. primitive

l. uniting

m. sticky

n. having to do with thoughts and feelings

o. explosive fuel

p. agitator

q. contrary to what is intended

r. deadly

s. surveying instrument

t. greed

u. projectile

truncated (207)	tensile (213)	aperture (214)	parameters (217)
thermodynamics (248)	isentropic (248)	adiabatic (248)	elliptical (253)
trajectories (253)	overt (254)	ebullience (257)	flange (268)
guile (273)	syncopated (279)	translucent (281)	accolades (288)
converging (299)	diverging (299)		

Directions: The teacher will assign you one word from the list above. Turn to the page on which the word appears in the novel and examine how it is used in context. Complete the word map for your word and share your results with the class.

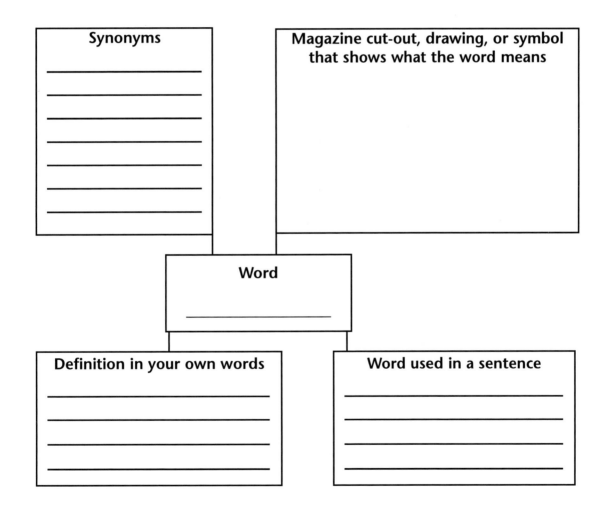

Name _____

dulcet (304)	inanely (308)	quest (316)	covertly (316)
marauded (328)	adamantly (340)	protocol (348)	ginseng (350)
wan (362)	lymph nodes (362)	effusive (373)	intrepid (374)
ablative (374)	maria (390)	dictum (416)	parabola (418)

Directions: Write each vocabulary word in the correct column below.

Parts of Speech

Noun	Verb	Adjective	Adverb

Name _____

Directions: Answer the following questions on a separate sheet of paper. Starred questions indicate thought or opinion questions. Use your answers in class discussions, for writing assignments, and to review for tests.

Chapter 1, pp. 1–16

1. What is the setting of the book (place and time period)? Who is the narrator and how old is he when his memoir begins?

2. *What does the company own in Coalwood? What do you think this implies?

3. What "Indian" tribe does Sonny invent? What do the Indians do? Why do they disband?

4. *What one thing did every Coalwood family have to have? Do you think this was a fair stipulation?

5. *How old was Homer Hickam, Sr. when he started working in the coal mine? How do you think his work affects his family?

6. Who is Poppy and what happened to him?

7. *Who are the "Great Six"? What effect do you think they have on Sonny?

8. *Describe Elsie Hickam's mural. What do you think this symbolizes to her?

Chapter 2, pp. 17–44

1. Where did Sonny get his nickname?

2. Who makes up Sonny's core group of friends? Briefly describe these friends.

3. *What date divides Sonny's life into two distinct phases? Why? Why do you think this event has such an impact on him?

4. *Identify two differences between Jim and Sonny. How do you think Sonny feels about Jim?

5. *Why have Jim and Sonny entered into a truce? Explain why you do or do not think this truce will last.

6. Whom does Sonny consider to be the most beautiful girl in high school? How does he feel about her?

7. *Why is Big Creek High School's football team in danger of losing out on the chance to become state champions? Explain why you do or do not think this is fair.

8. *What comment does Coach Morgan make about Sonny's ability to play football? Explain how this would make you feel.

9. Why doesn't Sonny quit football on his own? What causes him to quit? What does he do then?

Name _____

10. How do the media react to *Sputnik*? How does the Hickam family react?

11. What inspires Sonny to build a rocket? What is the outcome?

12. ***Prediction:** What consequences will Sonny face after the rocket fiasco?

Chapters 3–4, pp. 45–70

1. *How do Sonny's mother and father react to his first rocket launch? How would your parents or guardians have reacted?

2. What question does Sonny's mother ask him after the rocket failure? How does he reply? What does she tell him then?

3. *During their conversation about building a rocket, what question does Sonny ask his mother concerning his father? How does she reply? Why do you think Sonny asks this?

4. How does Buck Trant torment Sonny and his friends about the rocket? How does Sonny respond?

5. *What does Jim tell Sonny about the rocket failure? Why do you think he does this?

6. *How does Homer intervene in the football team's concerns? Why do you think he does this?

7. Briefly explain the conflict between John Dubonnet and Homer Hickam.

8. Why is being "cut-off" from work especially meaningful in Coalwood?

9. What does the X-ray reveal about Homer? How do Elsie and Sonny react?

10. ***Prediction:** How will Homer's illness affect him and his family?

11. ***Prediction:** Will the union/management conflict lead to violence?

Chapter 5, pp. 71–87

1. *Describe Quentin and tell why Sonny asks him to be part of his rocket group.

2. *How does Quentin respond to Sonny? How does Sonny feel about Quentin? Do you think their reactions are justified? Why or why not?

3. Why does Quentin agree to help Sonny?

4. *How does Roy Lee react to Sonny's conversation with Quentin? What do you think Roy Lee's reaction implies?

5. Why does Sonny ask Dorothy to the dance? How does she respond?

6. *Briefly describe the company store and explain why you think this is an asset or a liability to the miners.

7. Who helps Sonny design the next two rockets? What are the results? How do Sonny's parents react?

8. According to Quentin, what is a "basis for modification"?

Name _____

9. *How does Sonny feel about Dorothy? How does she feel about him? How do you think their relationship will develop in the future?

Chapters 6–7, pp. 88–128

1. Who is Daisy Mae and why is she important to Sonny?

2. *After Sonny watches the successful ABMA rocket launch on TV, what does he tell Homer? How does Homer respond? Why do you think Homer's response is important to Sonny?

3. For what does the acronym BCMA stand? Who are the initial members and what role does each one fulfill? What is their goal?

4. *Why do Buck and other football players accost Sonny and Quentin? How does Jim respond? Why? How would you feel if you were Sonny?

5. Identify Mr. Turner and Miss Riley. How do they react to Quentin's "dream" of a science trophy?

6. *What does Emily Sue tell Sonny about his love for Dorothy? Explain why you do or do not agree with Emily Sue's assessment of Dorothy.

7. How does Isaac Bykovski help Sonny and the BCMA? How does Bykovski rationalize his help?

8. *What name do the boys choose for their rockets? Look up the meaning of the word and explain why you do or do not think this name is appropriate.

9. Where does *Auk IV* land? What problems does this cause?

10. *What does Homer do after hearing Rev. Lanier's sermon about fathers and sons? Why do you think he does this?

11. *Prediction: What effect will the construction of Cape Coalwood have on the BCMA? on the relationship between Homer and Sonny?

Chapters 8–9, pp. 129–162

1. *What two major announcements does Mr. Turner make to the Big Creek High School student body at the end of the 1957–58 school year? Which one do you think will have the most impact? Why?

2. What effect does the suspension of the football team have on Buck Trant? on Jim Hickam?

3. From whom does Sonny get equipment for Cape Coalwood?

4. Who is Jake Mosby? How does Sonny first meet him? How does Jake help the BCMA?

5. *What two things does Jake Mosby say every woman wants? Explain why you agree or disagree.

6. *Why is the friendship between Jake and Sonny unlikely? Why do you think their friendship develops?

7. What is the result of the launch of *Auk V*? How do the spectators react? How do the BCMA boys react?

8. What modification does Mr. Dubonnet suggest to Sonny following the launch of *Auk V*? What two problems do the boys need to address?

9. *How does Sonny compare his life in Coalwood with the capabilities of Jake's telescope? Why do you think he does so?

Chapters 10–11, pp. 163–205

1. How are the football boys different at the beginning of the 1958 school year?

2. What is Sonny's "startling revelation" about geometry? Who helps him understand his revelation?

3. *Why does the BCMA conflict with the law? How is the conflict resolved? Explain why you do or do not think Mr. Van Dyke really intends to press charges.

4. How does Sonny's view of academics change due to the BCMA?

5. *Who is the chemistry teacher at Big Creek High School? How would you rate her effectiveness as a teacher? Why?

6. Who is the new member of the BCMA? How does Elsie treat him?

7. What is "rocket candy"? What effect does it have on the rocket launches?

8. What height does *Auk XII* attain? After the launches of *Auks IX–XIII*, what do the boys realize is the major problem?

9. Why does Homer take Sonny into the mine? How do Sonny, Homer, and Elsie react to this experience?

10. *Prediction: What will be the eventual outcome of the black spot on Homer's lung?

Chapters 12–13, pp. 206–245

1. *How does Elsie punish Sonny for going into the mine with Homer? What does she vow to do if he ever goes again? Explain why you do or do not think she is serious.

2. *What two "drawers" does Sonny have in his mind? Which one is closed? Which one is open? Why do you think he refers to these as drawers?

3. How does Sonny cope with the open drawer? What is the result?

4. Who agrees to help Sonny with the welding on the rockets? What does he want in return for his help?

5. Who assumes the task of welding the rockets?

6. What is the most successful rocket in this section? How high does it go?

7. *What does Elsie give Sonny for Christmas? What do you think this symbolizes to Elsie? to Sonny?

8. *What does Miss Riley give Sonny? Quote her statement relating to the gift and to his reaction to the gift. What do you think she means by this?

9. What does Geneva Eggers do for Sonny? How does Homer explain his acquaintance with her to Sonny?

10. *Prediction: Will Sonny's love for Dorothy ever be reciprocated?

11. *Prediction: Will Sonny enter the science fair? If so, what will be the result?

Chapters 14–16, pp. 246–273

1. What is the altitude range that *Auks XVI–XIX* attain? What observation do the boys make?

2. Why do Sonny and Quentin want to take calculus and learn differential equations?

3. *Why does Mr. Hartsfield initially see no hope for having a calculus class at Big Creek High School? Do you think his opinion is justified?

4. What do the state troopers think the BCMA boys have done? How does Miss Riley assist the boys? What does Quentin prove?

5. What does the launch of *Auk XX* prove to the boys?

6. Why is Sonny not allowed to take calculus? How does Sonny plan to solve the problem?

7. *Explain why Sonny's problem with the calculus class is an example of irony.

8. What is the primary reason Quentin believes Sonny should enter the science fair?

9. *What does Elsie add to her mural during Homer's intense demands from the coal mine? What do you think this symbolizes?

10. What is Sonny's response to Homer's statement that he might come to Cape Coalwood when he has time? What does the ensuing confrontation reveal about Homer? about Sonny?

11. *State two reasons Sonny decides to enter the science fair. Which of the two reasons do you think is most valid?

12. *Prediction: Do you think the conflict between Homer and Sonny will ever be successfully resolved?

Chapters 17–19, pp. 274–301

1. *What causes Sonny's dreams of reciprocal love from Dorothy to end? Explain how you would feel if you were Sonny.

2. Who consoles Sonny after Dorothy dates Jim? How?

3. *What happens to Ike Bykovski and Homer in the mine tragedy? Which do you think most affects Sonny? Why?

4. *What effect does the tragedy have on Homer and Elsie? Why do you think this happens?

5. Why does Sonny abandon rocket building after the mine tragedy? How is the situation resolved?

6. What does Miss Riley tell Sonny about his rocket building?

Chapters 20–21, pp. 302–335

1. *Why does Miss Riley ask Sonny about Jake Mosby? Why do you think Sonny lies to her?

2. What money-making project does O'Dell suggest? What is the financial result?

3. What happens to Sonny on their money-making venture? What effect does this have on the Hickam family relationships?

4. What develops between the union and the company?

5. What do the BCMA boys decide to add to zinc and sulfur to create rocket fuel? Where do they get this ingredient? What do they call their new rocket fuel?

6. What is the name of the first rocket using the new fuel? How high does it go?

7. *What happens to *Auk XXII–D*? What are the results? What do you think this reveals about Homer?

8. **Prediction:** What effect will the incident at Cape Coalwood have on Homer? on the BCMA?

9. **Prediction:** Will Homer ever come to Cape Coalwood to watch Sonny launch a rocket?

Chapters 22–23, pp. 336–383

1. *Identify three changes in Sonny's life and Big Creek High School at the beginning of the 1959–1960 school year. Which one do you think has the most impact on Sonny?

2. Who does the calculations for the first rocket based on the sum total of Miss Riley's book? Why does he do so?

3. What is Quentin's definition of a good rocket?

4. What discovery solves the BCMA's financial problems?

5. Identify two results of the union/company conflict that directly affect the Hickam family and one that affects the BCMA. Are these resolved and, if so, how?

6. *What happens to Daisy Mae? How does Sonny feel? Do you think he should feel this way?

7. How does Elsie plan to pay for a house in Myrtle Beach?

8. *Why does Miss Riley choose Sonny to represent the BCMA at the science fair? How does he feel about this? Explain why you agree or disagree with her choice.

9. Why don't the BCMA boys think they have a chance to win the county science fair?

10. *What physical symptoms does Sonny begin to experience? What do you think causes his illness? How is the illness cured?

11. *Prediction: Will Homer and Elsie move to Myrtle Beach?

12. *Prediction: Will Miss Riley be able to finish the school year?

Chapter 24–Epilogue, pp. 384–428

1. Who insists that Sonny get a new suit for the National Science Fair? What is the result?

2. *What question does Sonny ask John F. Kennedy? How does Kennedy respond and what is Sonny's reply? What do you think this indicates about Kennedy?

3. What excuse does Homer give Elsie about not leaving Coalwood for Myrtle Beach?

4. With whom does Sonny become friends at the National Science Fair? How does this friend help Sonny?

5. What complication does Sonny face at the National Science Fair? How is it resolved? What is the result of the fair?

6. How does Sonny miss meeting Dr. Wernher von Braun in Indianapolis?

7. *What does Sonny do with the medal he receives in Indianapolis? Why do you think he does this?

8. *What does Sonny learn about his father's role in his win at the National Science Fair? What are the ramifications of his father's decision? What do you think this reveals about Homer?

9. How many rockets do the boys launch during their final act as the BCMA? What range do the rockets attain?

10. Who lights the fuse for the final rocket? Why? How does Sonny react?

11. What does the author reveal about each of the BCMA boys in the Epilogue? about Jim? about Miss Riley? about Homer and Elsie Hickam?

Name _____

Attribute Web

Directions: Place "Big Creek Missile Agency" in the center oval. Place the names of each member on the six long lines. On the smaller lines, record his role and two descriptive words.

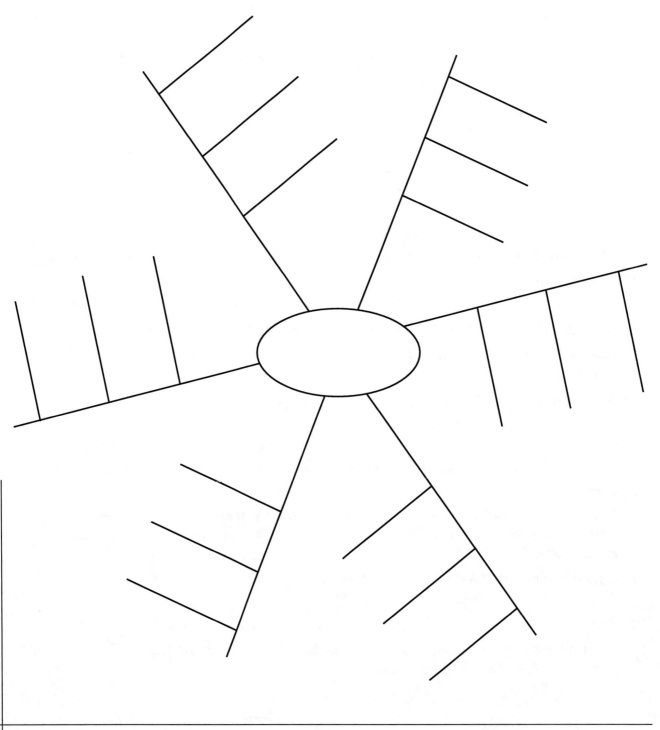

Name _____

Feelings

Directions: Complete the following chart for Homer "Sonny" Hickam, Jr. Record events that reflect his feelings about rocket building.

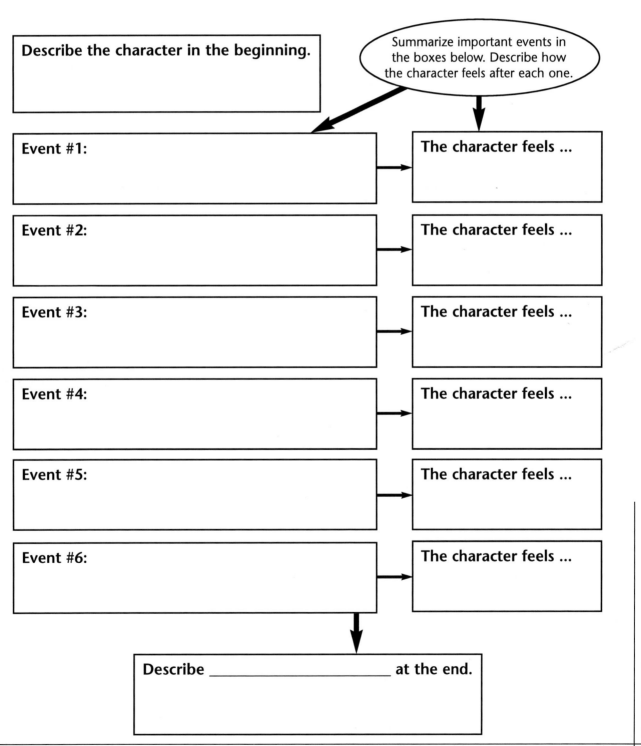

Name _____

Character Chart

Directions: Place the names Homer Hickam, Sr., Elsie Hickam, Jim Hickam, and Miss Riley in the boxes across the top. In the boxes across from each of the feelings, describe an incident or time in the book when each character experienced that feeling. You may use "not applicable" if you cannot find an example.

Frustration				
Anger				
Fear				
Humiliation				
Relief				

Name _____

Cause/Effect Chart

Directions: Choose an incident from the book and identify the cause of the incident and its effects (e.g., Russia's launch of *Sputnik*, football team's suspension, etc.).

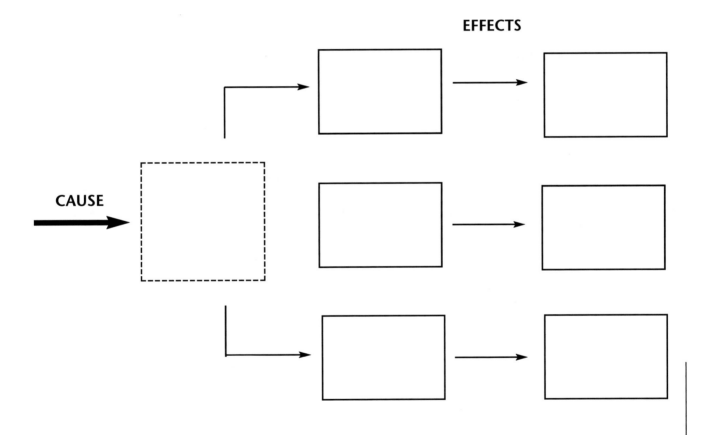

Name _____

Story Map

Characters _____

_____

Setting

Time and Place _____

_____

↓

Problem

Problem _____

_____

_____

↓

Goal

Goal _____

_____

_____

↓

Episodes

Beginning ⟶ Development ⟶ Outcome

_____

_____

_____

_____

↓

Resolution

Resolution _____

_____

_____

_____

Inference Flow Chart

Directions: Fill in the boxes of the flow chart with the events portrayed in the story. In the ovals beneath, state what emotions and feelings are inferred.

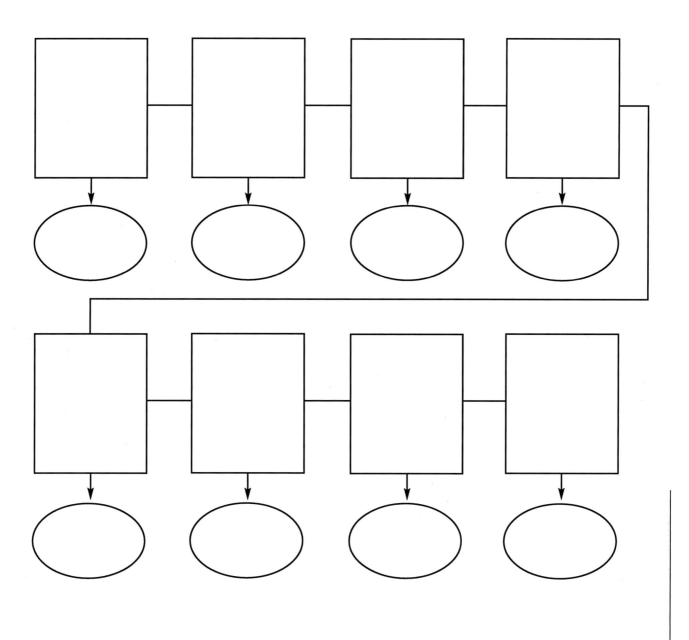

Name _____

Bio-poem

Directions: Homer "Sonny" Hickam, Jr. is the narrator of the memoir. What kind of person is he? What values does he have that you share? Using the format below, write a bio-poem about Sonny. After you have written a bio-poem about Sonny, write one about yourself.

—Line 1: First name only
—Line 2: Lover of (list three things character loves)
—Line 3: Giver of (list three things character gives)
—Line 4: Needs (list three things character needs)
—Line 5: Wants (list three things character wants)
—Line 6: Is good at (list three things character is good at)
—Line 7: Should work on (list three things character needs to improve)
—Line 8: Is similar to (list three people or other characters to whom this character is similar—list a reason behind each character, for example: Is similar to Sonny from *October Sky* because he is young and interested in science)
—Line 9: Survivor of (list three things the character survives)
—Line 10: Last name only

Title _____

1. _____
2. _____
3. _____
4. _____
5. _____
6. _____
7. _____
8. _____
9. _____
10. _____

Conflict

The **conflict** of a story is the struggle between two people or two forces. There are three main types of conflict: person vs. person, person vs. nature or society, and person vs. self.

Directions: Working in a small group, define the words conflict, compromise, cooperation, and control. Complete the following chart outlining one of the book's conflicts (e.g., Homer/Sonny, Homer/Elsie, Sonny/Jim). Share your completed chart with the class.

Character: _____

Conflict	Resolution

Character: _____

Conflict	Resolution

Character: _____

Conflict	Resolution

Name _____

A. Matching: Match the following characters with the correct identification.

____ 1. Homer Hickam, Sr.

____ 2. Elsie Hickam

____ 3. Sonny Hickam

____ 4. Jim Hickam

____ 5. "Little" Richard

____ 6. Roy Lee

____ 7. John Dubonnet

____ 8. Quentin

a. most socially outgoing member of the Rocket Boys

b. arrogant, belligerent football player

c. union leader

d. minister of a small church

e. intelligent; class nerd

f. thinks his father doesn't like him

g. paints a mural portraying a dream

h. works hard; leaves little time for family

B. True/False: Indicate whether each statement is true or false.

____ 9. The mining company owns almost everything in Coalwood except the church to which the majority of the people belong.

____10. Elsie Hickam shares her husband's love for mining.

____11. Sonny and Jim call a truce because their sibling rivalry escalates into a danger zone.

____12. Sonny and his friends decide to launch their first rocket by the fence.

____13. Dorothy gladly accepts Sonny's invitation for a date.

____14. Hickam presents a positive picture of Coalwood's company store.

____15. Quentin is disheartened by the failure of the first two rockets he helps build.

Name _____

Short Answer: Write a brief answer to each of the following questions.

1. Who names the Big Creek Missile Agency?

2. Who first suggests that the boys enter the science fair?

3. Why doesn't Sonny want to enter the science fair?

4. Who welds the rockets for Sonny?

5. What name does Sonny give to all the rockets?

6. Why does Sonny agree to launch *Auk IV* close to the mine?

7. What is the name of the BCMA's "home"?

8. What primary effect does *Sputnik* have on Big Creek High School?

9. Why is Jake Mosby in Coalwood?

10. How does Mosby react to the launch of *Auk V*? Why?

11. What do the rocket boys name their new propellant?

12. Identify the new member of the rocket boys' group.

13. How do Roy Lee and O'Dell create problems for the BCMA?

14. How do the football boys take out their anger on the BCMA?

15. Why does Homer take Sonny into the mine? How does Elsie react?

Name _____

A. Fill in the Blanks: Write the word(s) that correctly completes each statement.

1. Isaac Bykovski convinces _____ to help Sonny.

2. _____ assumes the task of welding the rockets after Isaac

    Bykovski's death.

3. Elsie gives Sonny _____

    _____ for Christmas.

4. _____ rescues Sonny from the freezing cold.

5. State troopers accuse the BCMA boys of _____.

6. After Sonny is denied admittance to the calculus class, he decides to _____

    _____.

7. After the mine tragedy, Miss Riley tells Sonny he must put aside his hurt and anger so

    _____.

8. Mrs. Bykovski tells Sonny he should _____ in honor of Ike.

B. True/False: Indicate whether each statement is true or false.

____ 9.   Sonny takes Dorothy to the Christmas formal.

____ 10. Miss Riley gives Sonny a book about guided missile design.

____ 11. Sonny is not allowed to take the calculus class because the teacher is convinced he
          cannot learn.

____ 12. Quentin tells Sonny the rocket boys view him as their ticket to college.

____ 13. Anger toward his dad is a key factor in Sonny's decision to enter the science fair.

____ 14. Sonny realizes the futility of his love for Dorothy when she dates his brother.

____ 15. Sonny initially reacts to the mine tragedy by intensifying his rocket building.

A. Short Answer: Write a brief answer to each of the following questions.

1. What is O'Dell's "treasure"?

2. What happens to Sonny on the BCMA's money-making venture?

3. What do the BCMA boys add to zinc and sulfur to create rocket fuel?

4. What does Sonny call the rocket fuel made from John Eye's alcohol?

5. How does Elsie plan to pay for a house in Myrtle Beach?

6. Why does Miss Riley choose Sonny to represent the BCMA at the science fair?

7. What suggestion does Sonny make to President-nominee John F. Kennedy?

8. What major complication occurs with Sonny's display at the National Science Fair? How is it resolved?

B. True/False: Indicate whether each statement is true or false.

_____ 9. After *Auk XXII–D* lands in Coalwood, Homer orders Cape Coalwood to be destroyed.

_____ 10. Union/company tension is eased during the launch of *Auk XXV*.

_____ 11. Sonny blames himself for Daisy Mae's death.

_____ 12. Sonny gives his National Science Fair medal to Dorothy.

_____ 13. Homer refuses to sign the union/company agreement that will end the strike.

_____ 14. Sonny asks his father to light the final rocket.

_____ 15. Homer Hickam, Jr. fulfills his youthful dream of becoming a NASA engineer.

A. Identification: Match each character to the correct description. (1 pt. each)

____ 1. Sonny Hickam

____ 2. Jim Hickam

____ 3. Homer Hickam, Sr.

____ 4. Elsie Hickam

____ 5. Quentin

____ 6. Freida Joy Riley

____ 7. Jake Mosby

____ 8. John Dubonnet

____ 9. Dorothy Plunk

___ 10. Isaac Bykovski

___ 11. Emily Sue Buckleberry

___ 12. Dr. Wernher von Braun

a. encouraging mother; dreams of a more serene life

b. class nerd who touts his intelligence

c. Sonny's concept of "God's perfection"

d. invites a reporter to view a BCMA rocket launch

e. overworked father; shows favoritism for one son

f. a dreamer; yearns for father's approval

g. risks job status to help a young rocket builder

h. first inspires Sonny to build a rocket

i. arrogant, athletic, self-centered

j. true friend who tries to open Sonny's eyes to reality

k. an encouraging teacher

l. union leader

B. Multiple Choice: Choose the BEST answer. (2 pts. each)

___ 13. During Sonny Hickam's childhood, his mother instills in him the idea that
(a) he is better than other Coalwood children
(b) he is not just like his father
(c) no one has the right to tell him what to do
(d) he is not as capable as his brother

___ 14. Sonny Hickam categorizes his life in West Virginia into two distinct phases, before and after
(a) October 5, 1957
(b) meeting Dorothy Plunk
(c) his father's job as superintendent of the mine
(d) December 25, 1958

___ 15. Sonny and Jim Hickam conflict over all BUT which of the following?
(a) Sonny's participation in the high school band
(b) Sonny's rocket adventures
(c) Jim's desire to become a football coach
(d) the football team's suspension

___ 16. Homer and Elsie's quarrels usually revert to conflict about
(a) Homer's favoritism for Jim
(b) the mine
(c) Elsie's spending habits
(d) Geneva Eggers

___ 17. Sonny's mother wants him to build a rocket
(a) to prove he is as intelligent as Jim
(b) so he can buy them a home in Myrtle Beach
(c) to demonstrate the intelligence of the Lavender family
(d) to prove his father is wrong and she is right

___ 18. Homer creates problems for Big Creek High School's football team
(a) by filing a lawsuit against the state high school athletic association
(b) because the coach has treated Jim unfairly
(c) because the coach will not allow Sonny to play
(d) by withdrawing funds provided by the mine

___ 19. Quentin agrees to help Sonny build a rocket because
(a) Sonny has leadership qualities Quentin doesn't have
(b) Sonny is the most intelligent boy Quentin knows
(c) Quentin needs to make the money
(d) Sonny threatens to beat him up if he doesn't

___ 20. When the football boys are harassing Sonny and Quentin in front of the trophy case, Jim intervenes because
(a) of his affection for Sonny
(b) he thinks it is unfair to pit two against so many
(c) he doesn't want the team to get in trouble
(d) he has promised his mother he would look after Sonny

___ 21. Isaac Bykovski thinks Sonny should tell his father about the work on the rockets in the welding shop because
(a) he doesn't want to get in trouble
(b) he doesn't want Sonny to get in trouble
(c) he's afraid he will lose his job
(d) Homer should be proud of what they are doing

___ 22. After *Auk IV* lands in Coalwood, Homer
  (a) tells Sonny he must pay for the damage to the office
  (b) reassigns Bykovski to the mine
  (c) sends Sonny to live with his grandparents
  (d) cuts off Sonny's allowance

___ 23. Homer changes his mind about Sonny's rocket building and gives him land for a launch pad
  (a) after Rev. Lanier's sermon
  (b) because Elsie threatens to leave
  (c) after getting permission from the owner of the coal mine
  (d) when he recognizes Sonny's level of expertise

___ 24. One problem the BCMA needs to address after launching *Auk V* is
  (a) how to conserve rocket fuel
  (b) how to make rockets fly straight
  (c) what to do with excess fuel
  (d) the need to develop a better fuse

___ 25. After going into the mine with his father, Sonny
  (a) understands Homer's love for the mine
  (b) promises Homer he will consider becoming a miner
  (c) is afraid for Homer to continue working at the mine
  (d) rebels against his mother

___ 26. The most treasured Christmas gift Sonny has ever received is
  (a) the scale-model of a rocket
  (b) an autographed picture of Dr. Wernher von Braun
  (c) his dad's Buick
  (d) a book on rocket design

___ 27. The two things that force Sonny to fight for his life in freezing weather are
  (a) Dorothy's love and Quentin's faith in him
  (b) the fear of death and his mother's love
  (c) rockets to build and Dorothy to win
  (d) rockets to build and Homer's approval to win

___ 28. After hearing Homer's story of Geneva Eggers, Sonny
  (a) is proud of him for a long-ago act of heroism
  (b) is ashamed of his dad's cowardice
  (c) believes Homer is in love with Geneva
  (d) immediately repeats the story to Elsie

___ 29. Miss Riley comes to the BCMA boys' defense when
  (a) they are accused of theft
  (b) Mr. Turner refuses to allow them to go to the science fair
  (c) the football boys harass them
  (d) they are accused of starting a forest fire

___ 30. Sonny is not allowed to take the calculus class because
     (a) he has not had enough prerequisites
     (b) Mr. Hartsfield doesn't like him
     (c) seven apply for a six-student class, and his grades are the lowest
     (d) Dorothy Plunk convinces Mr. Turner she needs it more than Sonny

___ 31. Sonny's ongoing conflict involves
     (a) his father's rejection and his brother's harassment
     (b) not knowing who he is and what he's supposed to do
     (c) Dorothy's rejection and his desire to build rockets
     (d) all of the above

___ 32. Sonny makes his final decision to enter the science fair because
     (a) he knows he can win
     (b) he wants to repay his mother for her faith in him
     (c) he knows Miss Riley is dying
     (d) he wants to show his father he can do it

___ 33. Sonny realizes the futility of his love for Dorothy
     (a) when she has a date with Jim
     (b) when she tells him she can never love him
     (c) after he realizes she undermined him to get in the calculus class
     (d) after Roy Lee tells him the truth about her

___ 34. Which of the following is NOT a result of the mine tragedy?
     (a) Isaac Bykovski dies.
     (b) Homer's eye is irreparably damaged.
     (c) Homer is credited with saving 12 lives.
     (d) The Hickam family bonds more closely.

___ 35. After the mine tragedy, Miss Riley tells Sonny
     (a) she sympathizes with his deep anguish
     (b) he needs to take a few weeks away from building rockets
     (c) he must put aside his hurt and anger so he can do his job
     (d) she is in much worse condition than he, yet she still keeps going

___ 36. Quentin's definition of a good rocket is
     (a) one that soars two miles
     (b) one from which they can develop a basis of modification
     (c) one that does precisely what it's designed to do
     (d) one that doesn't hurt anyone

___ 37. Sonny is best described as
     (a) a pessimist
     (b) an optimist
     (c) a hypocrite
     (d) delusional

___ 38. The BCMA's financial problems are solved
  (a) with the discovery of zincoshine
  (b) after they recover 400 pounds of scrap iron
  (c) when the town takes up a collection for them
  (d) with the discovery of ginseng

___ 39. Sonny abandons his plans for revenge over Daisy Mae's death because
  (a) Roy Lee can't discover who killed her
  (b) he believes Coalwood justice will take care of it
  (c) his mother begs him to let it go
  (d) Rev. "Little" convinces him revenge is not the answer

___ 40. While in Welch to purchase a new suit, Sonny has an encounter with
  (a) Hubert Humphrey
  (b) Dr. Wernher von Braun
  (c) Robert Kennedy
  (d) President-nominee John F. Kennedy

___ 41. A complication at the National Science Fair occurs when
  (a) someone steals parts to Sonny's rocket
  (b) the committee refuses to consider propulsion as a separate entity
  (c) Sonny loses all his money
  (d) someone steals Sonny's display panels

___ 42. In order to help Sonny at the National Science Fair, Homer
  (a) allows Caton to weld the rocket parts even though the strike is not settled
  (b) travels to Indianapolis to help Sonny
  (c) signs the union/management agreement
  (d) sends Sonny extra money

___ 43. Homer's reaction after he lights the fuse for the BCMA's final rocket reflects
  (a) pure delight
  (b) happiness, pain, and fear
  (c) pride in Sonny
  (d) sorrow, pain, and fear

___ 44. Which of the following is NOT revealed in the Epilogue?
  (a) All the rocket boys go to college.
  (b) Miss Riley dies.
  (c) Sonny becomes a NASA engineer.
  (d) Sonny never reconciles with Jim.

___ 45. "Coal is the life blood of this country" is an example of
  (a) simile
  (b) allusion
  (c) metaphor
  (d) personification

___ 46. In the book, references to Valley Forge and Pearl Harbor are examples of
     (a) allusion
     (b) simile
     (c) metaphor
     (d) irony

___ 47. "The steel casement was turned back like a banana peel" is an example of
     (a) metaphor
     (b) simile
     (c) personification
     (d) allusion

C. Essay: Answer one of the following in a well-developed essay. (10 pts.)

  a. Explain how the theme of perseverance is developed in the novel.

  b. Explain the transformation of the relationship between Sonny and his father.

  c. Explain how Elsie Hickam and Miss Riley influence Sonny's life.

D. Creative Response: Complete one of the following. (8 pts.)

  a. Write an acrostic for the "Great Six." Place the phrase vertically on your paper, then write a descriptive phrase beginning with each letter.

  b. Write a poem about rejection that references situations in the book.

  c. Write a newspaper feature article about the final rocket launch. Include quotes from those involved.

Name _____

A. Identification: Complete the following chart for the members of the BCMA. (2 pts. each)

Character	Primary Characteristics	Role in the BCMA
1. Homer Hickam, Jr.		
2. Sherman		
3. O'Dell		
4. Roy Lee		
5. Quentin		
6. Billy		

B. Identification: List two characteristics of each character and explain his or her reaction to Sonny Hickam's dream. (2 pts. each)

Character	Primary Characteristics	Reaction
7. Homer Hickam, Sr.		
8. Elsie Hickam		
9. Freida Joy Riley		
10. Isaac Bykovski		
11. Dr. Wernher von Braun		
12. Jake Mosby		

C. Multiple Choice: Choose the BEST answer. (2 pts. each)

___ 13. Elsie Hickam's mural symbolizes
    (a) her dream of becoming an artist
    (b) her desire to change Coalwood into a beautiful town
    (c) her love for her family
    (d) her desire for a serene and secure life away from Coalwood

___ 14. Elsie wants Sonny to build a rocket for all BUT which of the following reasons?
    (a) to help him get out of Coalwood
    (b) to enable the family to buy a home in Myrtle Beach
    (c) to prove his father is wrong and she is right
    (d) to change Homer's mind about sending Sonny to college

___ 15. Ramifications of the launch of *Auk IV* include all BUT which of the following?
    (a) Elsie is upset with Homer for his reaction.
    (b) Elsie is upset with Sonny for getting Mr. Bykovski into trouble.
    (c) Homer accuses Sonny of being a thief.
    (d) Homer reassigns Bykovski to the mine.

___ 16. The Russians' launch of *Sputnik* results in all BUT which of the following?
    (a) establishment of NASA
    (b) restructuring of academic curriculum in U.S. schools
    (c) immigration of Dr. Wernher von Braun to the U.S.
    (d) media accolades for the educational status of Russian students

___ 17. Homer assists the BCMA by doing all BUT which of the following?
    (a) agrees to finance the building of *Auks X–XV*
    (b) allows them to use the machines in the mine's welding shop
    (c) supplies concrete for the launch pad
    (d) gives them land for Cape Coalwood

___ 18. Sonny's trip into the mine with Homer results in all BUT which of the following?
    (a) Sonny comes to understand his dad's love for the mine.
    (b) Homer reacts to Sonny in anger and disappointment.
    (c) Elsie angrily confronts Homer about the mine.
    (d) Sonny agrees to consider becoming a mining engineer.

___ 19. The landing of *Auk XXII–D* in Coalwood results in all BUT which of the following?
    (a) Mr. Fuller orders the launch pad bulldozed.
    (b) Homer and Elsie engage in a bitter verbal confrontation.
    (c) Sonny's vehement statement about Coalwood hurts his father.
    (d) Homer angrily confronts the mine's general superintendent.

___ 20. When Sonny encounters President-nominee John F. Kennedy, he suggests the
United States should
(a) go to war with Russia
(b) allocate more money toward rocketry
(c) go to the moon
(d) provide more funds for college scholarships for future engineers

___ 21. Which of the following is NOT revealed in the Epilogue?
(a) All the rocket boys go to college.
(b) Homer Hickam, Jr. becomes a NASA engineer.
(c) Miss Riley dies.
(d) Homer Hickam, Jr. meets Dr. Wernher von Braun.

___ 22. Which of the following most appropriately refers to Sonny and the BCMA?
(a) dreaming and saying "Why not?"
(b) a dream deferred
(c) a thwarted dream
(d) dreaming big but settling for less

D. Short Answer: On your own paper, write brief answers to the following questions.
(2 pts. each)

23. Into what two distinct phases does Sonny categorize his life?

24. What is the primary source of conflict between Homer and Elsie?

25. Identify three specific academic subjects the rocket boys realize they need to understand
after they begin to build rockets.

26. Why does Sonny consider Ike Bykovski to be an "open drawer" in his mind?

27. What is the most treasured Christmas gift Sonny has ever received? Who gives it to him?

28. What two things cause Sonny to force himself to continue moving when in freezing
conditions?

29. Explain why Sonny's not being allowed to take calculus is an example of irony.

30. What two things does Sonny's ongoing mental conflict involve?

31. What primary motivation causes Sonny to enter the science fair?

32. State two results of the mine tragedy that directly affect Sonny.

33. What two reasons does Miss Riley give Sonny for continuing to build rockets?

34. What is Quentin's definition of a good rocket?

35. Identify two personal attacks against the Hickam family caused by the
union/company strife.

36. What does Homer do in order to help Sonny at the National Science Fair? How does this change the lives of Homer and Elsie?

37. "[Sonny is]...our [the BCMA boys']...ticket to college" is an example of what literary device?

38. "...the stars were spread out like diamonds on a vast blanket of black velvet" is an example of what literary device?

39. Identify the tone of the memoir.

40. Identify the mood of the memoir.

E. Essay: Answer one of the following in a well-developed essay. (10 pts.)

   a. Homer Hickam, Jr. has stated, "There's a plan. If you are willing to fight hard enough, you can make it detour for awhile, but you're still going to end up where God wants you to be." Based on this statement, explain whether or not you think Hickam believes in destiny. Cite examples from the book to support your opinion.

   b. Explain the impact on Sonny of Miss Riley's statement, "All I've done is give you a book. You have to have the courage to learn what's inside it." Include an analysis of her motivational methods.

   c. Identify and explain "detours" in Sonny's pursuit of his dream and how he circumvents them. Include what Sonny's actions say about his character.

F. Creative Response: Complete one of the following. (10 pts.)

   a. Write a poem reflecting Sonny's feelings about Daisy Mae's death.

   b. Write a eulogy for Miss Riley reflecting Homer Hickam, Jr.'s feelings about her.

   c. Write a newspaper article about the 25th class reunion of the Big Creek High School's graduating class of 1960.

Answer Key

Activities #1–2: Responses will vary.

Activity #3: Charts will vary.

Activity #4: 1. c 2. o 3. f 4. r 5. t 6. a 7. n 8. p 9. g 10. u 11. d 12. h 13. q 14. b 15. i 16. l 17. k 18. m 19. e 20. s 21. j

Activity #5: Charts will vary.

Activity #6: Nouns—quest, protocol, ginseng, lymph nodes, maria, dictum, parabola; Verbs—marauded; Adjectives—dulcet, wan, effusive, intrepid, ablative; Adverbs—inanely, covertly, adamantly

Study Guide

Chapter 1: 1. Coalwood, West Virginia; 1957–1960; Sonny Hickam, 14 years old 2. almost everything except the post office; Answers will vary. 3. Coalhicans; streak faces with berry juice, stick feathers in hair, conduct imaginary raids and massacres, "ambush" miners; Tony breaks his arm in a mock battle. 4. a father who worked for the mine company 5. 22; Answers will vary. 6. Sonny's paternal grandfather; got both legs cut off in mining accident 7. Coalwood's elementary teachers, grades 1–6; Answers will vary. 8. seashore with sand, shells, a lot of sky, a couple of seagulls; Answers will vary.

Chapter 2: 1. His mother began calling him "Sunny" because he was a happy child; 1st grade teacher changed it to "Sonny" 2. Roy Lee: thin, outgoing, popular; Sherman: compact, muscular, left leg shriveled from polio; O'Dell: small, excitable 3. October 5, 1957; Russians launched *Sputnik*; Answers will vary. 4. Jim: athletic, strong, dresses stylishly, attracts girls; Sonny: not athletic, smaller and sneakier, doesn't care how he dresses, doesn't have a girlfriend; Answers will vary. 5. both injured in ferocious fight that scared them both; Answers will vary. 6. Dorothy Plunk; thoughts of her consume him; thinks she is "God's perfection" 7. have played too many West Virginia teams; Answers will vary. 8. "Sonny's small, but he makes up for it by being slow." Answers will vary. 9. his mother's rule, "If you start something, you've got to finish it"; Coach orders him off football field; joins high school band 10. media: filled with stories about America's attempts to catch up with Russia; Sonny: feels as if watching science fiction come true; Jim and Homer: disinterested; Elsie: calls *Sputnik* a pretty thing when it passes over Coalwood 11. He wants to work for Dr. Wernher von Braun; decides to build a rocket; it blows up. 12. Answers will vary.

Chapters 3–4: 1. Elsie: disbelief but declares faith in Sonny; Homer: doesn't believe Sonny is capable of building a rocket; doesn't want Sonny to embarrass him; Answers will vary. 2. Elsie: Do you think you could build a rocket? Sonny: No, I don't know how. Elsie tells him to show his father he can. 3. Sonny: Why doesn't Dad like me? Elsie: not that his dad doesn't like him but he just never had much time to think about Sonny one way or the other; Answers will vary. 4. Buck: calls them little sister idiot morons; Sonny: asks about Buck's mother, who ran off with another man 5. tells Sonny everybody is laughing at the family because of him; Answers will vary. 6. hires a lawyer to file a lawsuit against the high school athletic association; Answers will vary. 7. Dubonnet is a union leader; he confronts Homer, a company man, because the company is laying off workers. 8. being cut-off means being cut off from homes, credit at the company store, and identification as a Coalwood citizen; must leave Coalwood in two weeks 9. spot the size of a dime on his lung; Elsie: alarmed, asks what he's going to do; Sonny: feels panicky 10. Answers will vary. 11. Answers will vary.

Chapter 5: 1. class nerd; intelligent; uses big words, carries overstuffed briefcase; Sonny thinks he's intelligent enough to build a rocket. 2. Quentin: suspicious; thinks Sonny wants to copy his homework; asks Sonny how he can build a rocket when he doesn't even know algebra; Sonny: irritated; reluctant for others to see them together, especially shaking hands; Answers will vary. 3. thinks Sonny has leadership qualities he doesn't have and can get materials 4. calls Quentin a moron; wants to know why Sonny is talking to him and "holding his hand" 5. because Roy Lee will ask her if he doesn't; says she already has plans but would love to study with him 6. has almost everything; fair prices; credit closely watched; fairly run; Answers will vary. 7. Quentin; first emits nasty smoke, then falls over; second blows up; father angry; mother tells him to find a better place 8. have to start somewhere and build as go along, whether success or failure; Answers will vary. 9. in love with her; wants to just be his friend; Answers will vary.

Chapters 6–7: 1. his cat; loves her, confides in her, always there for him 2. Sonny: rocket works; we're going into space; Homer: sometimes he thinks Sonny is already in space; thinks the rocket is wonderful; Answers will vary. 3. Big Creek Missile Agency; Sonny: president, O'Dell: treasurer, Roy Lee: transportation, Sherman: publicity and setting up rocket range, Quentin: scientist; to learn about and build rockets 4. They are standing in front of the trophy case; tells them to get filthy hands off; Jim: leave them alone because he doesn't want team to get in trouble; Answers will vary. 5. Turner: high school principal; says he will not tolerate a bomb in the school; Miss Riley: chemistry teacher; thinks trophy is a great idea and wants them to enter the science fair 6. Dorothy will never be more than a friend and she and Jim are alike, i.e., both searching for someone who will like them for themselves; Answers will vary. 7. offers advice; says he will teach Sonny to solder; builds three rockets; Homer should be proud of what goes on in the welding shop; Answers will vary. 8. *Auk* 9. at the coal company; tears a big chunk out of the office; Homer is angry; accuses Sonny of being a thief and reassigns Bykovski to the mine 10. gives Sonny land for rocket launch site and agrees to build blockhouse; Answers will vary. 11. Answers will vary.

Chapters 8–9: 1. football team is suspended for 1958 school year; academic curriculum will be restructured with no more easy classes; Answers will vary. 2. Buck: angry, teary-eyed, thinks he has no chance for scholarship; Jim: angry, accuses his dad of ruining everything and vows never to forgive him 3. from Mr. McDuff and Mr. Ferro 4. junior engineer at the mine; tries to sell him a newspaper; invites news reporter to rocket launch 5. to know that a man really loves her; that he isn't going to stop; Answers will vary. 6. difference in age and outlook on life; Answers will vary. 7. climbs 50 feet, turns toward spectators, slams into road; throw themselves to the ground; think they're making progress and give cheer similar to football players 8. allow powder to dry at least two weeks; how to make rockets fly straight and find a better way to send them off 9. telescope: can see million light years away but not focus on town telescope is in; Sonny: clear vision of his future in space, but life in Coalwood a blur

Chapters 10–11: 1. sullen, sensitive to insult; seem less muscled and less bright 2. that plane geometry is a message from God; Rev. Richard 3. O'Dell and Roy Lee try to take some old phones from mine property and are caught; they agree to pay for the phones and the damage; Answers will vary. 4. becomes more interested in chemistry and realizes need for upper-level courses; building rockets provides motivation to learn all he can 5. Miss Riley; Answers will vary. 6. Billy; gives him clothes and feeds him 7. rocket fuel made up of sugar and saltpeter; it causes the rocket nozzles to explode 8. 760 ft.; nozzle corroded; they need to build the rockets out of material that can withstand heat and oxidation 9. wants to convince him to become a mining engineer; Sonny: doesn't want to hurt his dad but still wants to be a space engineer; Homer: disappointed and angry because of Sonny's refusal; Elsie: furious that Sonny went into the mine with his father; publicly confronts Homer 10. Answers will vary.

Chapters 12–13: 1. takes back her kitchen hardware; makes him cook kidneys for the cats; shoot and kill him; Answers will vary. 2. his father (closed), what his dad told him about Ike Bykovski: von Braun had worked for the Germans and Ike is a Jew (open); Answers will vary. 3. goes to Bykovski and asks him about von Braun; Bykovski tells him von Braun should be blamed for helping monsters but there are concepts of forgiveness and redemption; gives Sonny permission to admire von Braun for what he has become 4. Mr. Ferro; wants a mudhole behind his house filled with gravel 5. Clinton Caton 6. *Auk XIV*; 3,000 ft. 7. an autographed picture of Dr. von Braun and a personal note from him; Answers will vary. 8. a book, *Principles of Guided Missile Design*; "All I've done is give you a book. You have to have the courage to learn what's inside it." Answers will vary. 9. saves him from the freezing cold; he saved her life from a burning house when she was a baby 10. Answers will vary. 11. Answers will vary.

Chapters 14–16: 1. 2,000 to 3,000 ft.; With regards to altitude, bigger isn't always better. 2. They need to learn about the equations that the book on rocket design discusses. 3. county superintendent will not approve calculus because Big Creek High School is a football school; Answers will vary. 4. start a forest fire; points out distance on map is farther than any rocket could have gone; fire was started by aeronautical flare 5. the need for seamless tubing for the rocket 6. seven sign up for class that only allows six students; Sonny's grades are the lowest of the seven. 7. He was the one who originally asked for the class; Dorothy, the girl he loves, is the one who takes his place. 8. It will give the BCMA boys a chance to get college scholarships. 9. a house on the beach; Answers will vary. 10. He always has time for Jim; Homer: thinks Sonny won't do anything he asks; disappointed and hurt because Sonny wants to work for von Braun; Sonny: inner conflict between what his father wants for him and his own dream; angrily decides to become tough like his dad 11. to please Miss Riley and show his father he can accomplish something; Answers will vary. 12. Answers will vary.

Chapters 17–19: 1. She has a date with Jim; Answers will vary. 2. Valentine; takes him to a parked car to have sex 3. Bykovski: dies; Homer: irreparable damage to his eye; Answers will vary. 4. She cares for him for three weeks, but when he returns to the mine, they become distant, rarely communicating. Elsie stays in her room most of the time; Homer stays at the mine. 5. feels guilty about Bykovski's death, stops caring about anything; Miss Riley tells him he's suffering from self-pity and pride and that he must put aside his hurt and anger so he can do his job. Mrs. Bykovski requests that he continue to launch the rockets to honor her husband. 6. that it is his job and it honors him and the school

Chapters 20–21: 1. They are dating, and she knows Sonny is well acquainted with him. Sonny figures he owes Jake a good recommendation. 2. dig up and sell cast iron drainage pipes for scrap iron; make $4.00 after deducting expenses 3. slices an artery in his wrist and almost bleeds to death; Homer and Elsie unite in mutual concern; Jim watches over him. 4. mine company decides to sell miners' houses, churches, and utilities; Van Dyke is fired for trying to get company to keep things the same; new general superintendent orders a big cut-off and many miners lose their jobs 5. alcohol; from John Eye, the local moonshiner; zincoshine 6. *Auk XXII–A*; flies out of sight, 5,776 ft 7. lands in Coalwood; Fuller orders the leveling of the BCMA's launch pad and erects a barbed wire fence around the site. Mr. Dubonnet and other miners defy Fuller's orders and rebuild the boys' blockhouse. When Fuller attempts to regain control, Homer forces him to back down. He then tells Sonny he can have anything he needs from the mine. Answers will vary. 8. Answers will vary. 9. Answers will vary.

Chapters 22–23: 1. Jim leaves for college; Miss Riley is ill with cancer; football team is off suspension; Sonny is a senior. Answers will vary. 2. Sonny; because Quentin pushes him to do so 3. one that does precisely what it's designed to do 4. ginseng 5. Family: someone fires a bullet into their house; Elsie announces they are going to Myrtle Beach to buy a house; someone runs over Daisy Mae; neither resolved. The BCMA: Mr. Caton is told he can no longer weld for them; resolved when he does so covertly 6. She is run over and killed; Sonny feels guilty for letting her out; Answers will vary. 7. with money she's saved and invested in the stock market 8. He's the one who knows the most; thinks it should be Quentin;

Answers will vary. 9. because they are from Big Creek High School 10. headaches and nausea; Answers will vary; resolved when he quits being angry and discovers who he is and what he is going to do 11. Answers will vary. 12. Answers will vary.

Chapter 24–Epilogue: 1. Emily Sue; He buys an orange suit, but she insists he exchange it for a dark blue one. 2. Sonny: what U.S. should do in space; Kennedy: what Sonny thinks; Sonny: go to the moon; Answers will vary. 3. must wait until strike is over so union won't think they ran him off 4. Tex; convinces committee to put propulsion in separate category 5. Someone steals parts to his rocket; Caton welds more and Elsie mails them to Sonny; Sonny wins first prize. 6. Von Braun comes to Sonny's display while he is searching for him in another area. 7. gives it to Miss Riley; Answers will vary. 8. He agreed to sign the union/company agreement so Caton could weld new parts for Sonny; Homer must remain in Coalwood to make sure company keeps agreement; Answers will vary. 9. six; 3,000 ft. to 31,000 ft. 10. Homer Hickam, Sr.; Sonny asks him to; puts his arm around Homer's shoulder and tells him no one ever launched a better rocket 11. all go to college; Roy Lee: banker; O'Dell: insurance and farming; Quentin, Billy, Sherman, Sonny: engineers; Jim: football coach; Miss Riley: dies at age 32; Elsie: moves to Myrtle Beach; Homer joins her when he retires, dies in 1989.

Activities #7–#14: Answers will vary.

Quiz #1: (A) 1. h 2. g 3. f 4. b 5. d 6. a 7. c 8. e **(B)** 9. F (p. 4) 10. F (p. 14) 11. T (pp. 21–23) 12. T (p. 41) 13. F (p. 77) 14. T (pp. 78–79) 15. F (p. 85)

Quiz #2: 1. Sonny Hickam 2. Miss Riley 3. thinks he would embarrass himself against Welch High School 4. Isaac Bykovski 5. *Auk* 6. doesn't think it will be successful 7. Cape Coalwood 8. restructuring of academics with harder classes and more homework 9. junior engineer for the mine 10. throws himself to the ground, trembles; says it is almost like being in Korea 11. rocket candy 12. Billy 13. get caught attempting to take old phones from mine property 14. tear the blockhouse apart 15. try to convince him to become mining engineer; angry, crying, confronts Homer; tells Sonny she'll kill him if he ever goes again

Quiz #3: (A) 1. Leon Ferro 2. Clinton Caton 3. an autographed picture of Dr. Wernher von Braun and a personal note from him 4. Geneva Eggers 5. starting a forest fire 6. learn on his own using his dad's book 7. He can do his job building rockets, to honor himself and the school. 8. keep building rockets **(B)** 9. F (p. 221) 10. T (pp. 231–232) 11. F (p. 261) 12. T (p. 270) 13. T (pp. 269–270) 14. T (pp. 278–280) 15. F (pp. 292–297)

Quiz #4: (A) 1. scrap iron 2. slices artery in wrist, nearly bleeds to death 3. alcohol 4. zincoshine 5. with money she's saved and invested in the stock market 6. believes he knows the most 7. United States should go to the moon 8. Someone steals parts to his rockets; Homer signs union/company agreement so Caton can rebuild the parts. **(B)** 9. F (pp. 331–336) 10. F (p. 374) 11. T (p. 376) 12. F (p. 405) 13. F (pp. 407–410) 14. T (pp. 420–421) 15. T (p. 422)

Final Test, Level One: (A) 1. f 2. i 3. e 4. a 5. b 6. k 7. d 8. l 9. c 10. g 11. j 12. h **(B)** 13. b (pp. 15–16) 14. a (pp. 18–19) 15. c (pp. 35, 57, 61) 16. b (p. 47) 17. d (pp. 51–52) 18. a (pp. 60–62) 19. a (p. 72) 20. c (pp. 93–94) 21. d (p. 107) 22. b (pp. 109–115) 23. a (pp. 123–128) 24. b (pp. 155–156) 25. a (pp. 201–205) 26. b (p. 223) 27. c (p. 236) 28. a (pp. 243–245) 29. d (pp. 259–260) 30. c (p. 261) 31. d (throughout) 32. d (pp. 269–270) 33. a (pp. 278–280) 34. d (p. 299) 35. c (p. 297) 36. c (p. 340) 37. b (inference) 38. d (pp. 350–351) 39. b (pp. 381–382) 40. d (pp. 389–390) 41. a (p. 400) 42. c (pp. 407–410) 43. b (p. 421) 44. d (p. 422) 45. c (p. 202) 46. a (p. 129) 47. b (p. 183) **C&D:** Responses will vary.

Final Test, Level Two: (A) Suggestions: 1. dreamer, motivated; president 2. muscular, slightly crippled; publicity 3. small, excitable; treasurer 4. good-looking, popular; handles transportation 5. intelligent, nerd; scientist 6. intelligent, quick; helps others **(B)** Suggestions: 7. overworked, demanding; apathetic, skeptical 8. pretty, understanding, determined; believes in and supports him 9. understanding, innovative; encourages, motivates 10. hard worker, risk taker; first to help with welding 11. brilliant, respected; encourages via note 12. handsome, wealthy; encourages, invites news reporter **(C)** 13. d (pp. 15–16) 14. b (pp. 51–52) 15. a (pp. 109–115) 16. c (pp. 129–132) 17. a (pp. 151–152) 18. d (pp. 201–205) 19. b (pp. 331–336) 20. c (pp. 389–390) 21. d (pp. 422–423) 22. a (inference) **(D)** 23. before and after *Sputnik*, October 5, 1957 24. the mine 25. trigonometry, analytical geometry, calculus 26. doesn't know how Bykovski feels about von Braun's work for Germany in WWII 27. an autographed picture of Dr. von Braun and a personal note; his mother 28. rockets to build and Dorothy to win 29. He is the one who requested and pressed for the class, yet he is eliminated from the class because the girl he loves has better grades and takes the last spot. 30. not knowing who he is and what he's supposed to do 31. wants to show his dad he can accomplish something good 32. Responses will vary. Bykovski dies, Homer seriously injured, Homer and Elsie distant 33. to honor himself and his school; because he has a job to do 34. one that does precisely what it's designed to do 35. bullet fired into home; Daisy Mae run over and killed 36. signs union/company agreement; gives his word and must stay; can't move to Myrtle Beach, so Elsie moves there ahead of him 37. metaphor (p. 270) 38. simile (p. 161) 39. candid, conversational 40. optimistic **E&F:** Responses will vary.